Published in 2008 by JERBOA BOOKS
PO BOX 333838  Dubai UAE
www.jerboabooks.com
ISBN 978-9948-431-46-6

Approved by the National Information Council UAE:
No 776 20 June 2007

Text: © Denys Johnson-Davies
Illustrations: © Judi Barrett-Lennard
Layout design: Will Hill

# A Pair of Hoopoes

Denys Johnson-Davies

*illustrations*

Judi Barrett-Lennard

This book would not have been possible
without the generous support of
Dubai Duty Free

A holy man told a story about himself when he was boy and was working as the servant of a rich man.

When I was a young boy I worked for a rich man as one of his many servants. On growing up I decided I would change my life, give up the world and its pleasures, and become a wanderer through God's wonderful lands. I told the rich man of my decision and he wished me good luck in the new life I had chosen. 'And here,' he said to me, 'are two dinars which I hope will be of use to you on your travels.'

Holding the two dinars in my hand, I thought I would give one of them away to charity and spend the other one on myself.

That very same day I travelled to the local town. There, in the market, I saw two hoopoes in a cage. The man who had caught them was hoping to sell them and was asking two dinars for the pair. I tried to bargain with him and offered him one dinar for the two birds. 'No,' the man told me, 'I will not sell for less than one dinar a bird.'

I therefore thought of buying just one of the birds so that I would be left with one dinar for myself.

When I thought about it, I realised that the two hoopoes were a pair, a male and a female. They were used to being together and that, by buying just one of them I would be separating them. So I spent my two dinars and bought the two hoopoes, saying to myself that God would surely look after my needs.

I felt that it would be dangerous to let them loose in the town where they might well be shot by some hunter or be trapped again. Also, they would not find enough to eat in the town. So I took them outside the town to a place where there were fields and trees.

I set them free and was pleased to see them flying off happily into a nearby tree, heavy with fruit.

The two birds thanked me for the kindness I had done them, after which one of them said to the other, 'This kind man has saved us from the misery we were suffering in the cage. We should somehow repay him for what he has done for us.'

'From where I am sitting, I can see a jar full of money buried down by the roots of this tree, should we not tell him of this so that he can benefit from such a treasure?'

I answered the hoopoes by saying, 'I cannot understand how you can see a jar of money hidden under the ground and yet you were unable to notice the net in which you were caught?'

'It is all a matter of luck,' answered one of the birds.

'We hoopoes have the special power of seeing what is under the ground. However, when luck wants that we do not see something, we become blind to it. So we didn't see the net that the hunter had set for us because it was our bad luck not to see it.'

'On the other hand, it is your good luck that has made us see this jar of money under the ground by this tree.'

I immediately dug under the tree and found the jar full of gold coins. 'Praise be to God,' I said, 'for giving you the power of seeing what is under the ground.'

To this one of the hoopoes replied, 'O wise young man, you should surely know that luck is all-powerful and that no man can go against it.'
I thanked the hoopoe birds and left to continue my wandering through God's wonderful lands, knowing He had indeed looked after my needs, as I had trusted He would.

DENYS JOHNSON-DAVIES has been called 'the pioneer translator of modern Arabic literature'. Recently he published an anthology of Modern Arabic Literature. He's also the author of some fifty children's books. The book 'Memories in Translation' tells the story of how he became interested in Arabic and provides amusing anecdotes about the many Arab writers he has known; the book is available in both English and Arabic. Denys received the Sheikh Zayed Award for 2007 as the Personality of the Year in recognition of his contribution to making Arabic literature known outside the Arab world. Jerboa Books has published a volume of his short stories under the title 'Open Season in Beirut'.

JUDI BARRETT-LENNARD, an Australian by birth, lives in Al Ain, United Arab Emirates with her husband and two sons on a sheep farm. Judi's work tends to depict traditional views of Arabia which she expresses through her paintings and children's book illustrations.

## Other children's books by Denys Johnson-Davies Published by Jerboa Books